Purple Ronnie's Star Signs

Also by Purple Ronnie

Purple Ronnie's Book of Love
☆
Purple Ronnie's Guide to Life
☆
The Smashing World of Purple Ronnie

Published in 1994 by Statics (London) Ltd,
41 Standard Road, London NW10 6HF
Tel: 081-965 3327

© 1994 Giles Andreae

ISBN 1-873922-13-2

Print origination by Diva Graphics

Printed in England by H P II Print Ltd
Unit 3, Royal London Estate, 29 North Acton Road,
London NW10 6PE

Words by: Giles Andreae
Pictures by: Janet Cronin
and Giles Andreae

☆ Introduction ☆

Star Signs are a brilliant way of finding out about someone's character. You can use them to discover anything you like including what everyone's secretest rude fantasies are.

But reading what's written in the stars can only be done by incredibly brainy people like me. After gazing for ages through my gigantic telescope and doing loads of complicated sums and charts and stuff I have been able to work out exactly what everyone in the world is really like.

This book lets you know about all my amazing discoveries. It tells you what you look like, who your friends are, how your love life is, what you're like at Doing It and who you should be Doing It with.

Everything I've written in this book is completely true.
Honest.

Love from

Purple Ronnie
xox

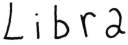

☆ Star File ☆

Aries
21st March - 20th April

Taurus
21st April - 20th May

Gemini
21st May - 20th June

Cancer
21st June - 22nd July

Leo
23rd July - 22nd August

Virgo
23rd August - 22nd September

Libra
23rd September - 22nd October

Scorpio
23rd October - 21st November

Sagittarius
22nd November - 21st December

Capricorn
22nd December - 19th January

Aquarius
20th January - 18th February

Pisces
19th February - 20th March

Aries

They like to be saucy and daring

And love to find trouble and danger

So talk about bosoms infront of their Mums

And show off their bottoms to strangers

Aries Looks

Aries people have a fun and happy look as if they are bubbling over with life. As soon as you look at an Aries they think you fancy them

Aries Men are strong and sexy. They have big bottoms and feet like plates. Their tongues often hang out and sometimes they dribble

Aries Women have a saucy way of looking at you. They have friendly smiles, sparkling eyes and they like wearing sexy outfits

Aries Character

Ariens are great fun to be with cos they love action and adventure and they always think up crazy ideas

Aries people love competitions and they get very
cross and grumpy if you don't let them win at everything

Aries and Friends

An Aries always has
loads of friends for
getting pissed with
and partying all
night long

Danger:- NEVER
tell an Aries
what to do or
they will shout
and scream
and kick you
in the goolies

Aries people would be good at being KING or QUEEN OF THE WORLD because:-

1. They love bossing everyone around and telling them what to do

O.K everyone follow me!

everybody listen to my super genius plan

SNOGGING TACTICS
A- find girl
B- give girl masses of booze
C- tell girl she is v. sexy
D- Snog girl

2. They are great at making clever plans

3. They are very brave and like nothing better than a good battle

take that you scallywag

Aries and Love

Secretly Ariens are worried that they're useless so you must tell them how gorgeously smashing and lovely they are all the time

Warning:- Always try to be as mysterious as possible or your Aries might run off with somebody else

Most of the time love with an Aries is fun and mad and very exciting

Aries and Sex

Ariens are completely sex-mad. They love Doing It in all sorts of places at any time of the day

⭐Secret Tip⭐ Aries people love the chase so you must never give in to them too quickly

Arien women love being on top and most of them eat men for breakfast

Taurus

Although they make good lovers
They don't give their love for free
If you ask them for a snog they say
"A snog - that's 20p"

Taurus Looks

Taurus people have firm sexy bodies but some are also short and stumpy

teeny lunchbox

Taurus Men think they are very tough and macho. They have thick muscly arms, hairy chests and small stubby doodahs. Some of them have silly beards

Taurus Women have tiny hands and feet, lovely soft skin and flat skinny bottoms. Sometimes they have quite round bodies but that does <u>not</u> mean that they are fat

skinny bot

Taurus Character

What Taurus people like most of all is to be safe and happy in a nice comfy place where everything is in order

extra soft lav paper

Taureans hate change and once they have found something they like, it is impossible to get them to try anything new

Taurus and Friends

Taurus people make gentle, kind and easy friends...

but they are not always very exciting

Danger :- Do not go anywhere near a Taurus who is angry

A Taurus would be a good COOK or GARDENER because:-

1. They love scrumptious food and they have very creative minds

extra boozy triple chocolate love cake →

2. They like beautiful things and are especially fond of plants and nature

la...la...la...

prrr

3. They love money and like to get paid for everything they do

come back soon

loads of cash

cheers

hic

Taurus and Love

Taureans are quite shy and they can take ages before making a move or pouncing on you

They are loving and faithful and they are good at old-fashioned type romance

Warning: - If you want to marry a Taurus you must be careful because they can get very boring when they're old

Taurus and Sex

A Taurus in love is unlikely ever to Do It with someone else but they can get incredibly jealous of their partners

Taurus people worry about their bodies even if they are very sexy

smelly candles

wiggle

masses of love cake

Taureans are brilliant at planning special nights of LOVE

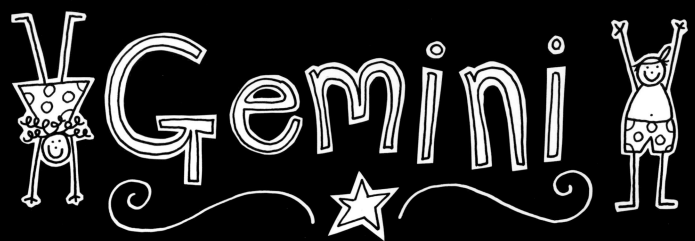

Gemini

Gemini people make wonderful friends
You can always break down on their shoulder
They tell you that crying
Is good now and then
And you come away wiser and older

Gemini Looks

As soon as you look at a Gemini they will wink at you, wiggle their bottoms and lick their lips

Gemini Men are tall and skinny when they're young and bald and porky when they're older. They love wriggling around and scratching their parts

Gemini Women always look younger than they are. They have sexy legs and they like to wear groovy clothes and fancy knickers

Gemini Character

Gemini people never seem to grow up. They love dashing around and trying out new things all the time

Geminis are also nervy and fidgety and completely useless at doing only one thing at a time

Gemini and Friends

Gemini people are great to have as friends because they are interested in practically everything

Warning:-

If you are a friend of a Gemini you must be very good at listening

total ↑
chatterbox

Gemini and Love

Geminis can go through lots of lovers because they want to find the <u>perfect</u> match

They love chatting people up and are quite likely to have naughty secret affairs

☆ Secret Tip ☆

Geminis don't like talking about deep feelings so if you go on a date with one you must be careful not to get too soppy

Gemini and Sex

Geminis like their sex
life to be fun and
playful and full of surprises

Sometimes Geminis get all
tangled up inside their heads
and what they need most is
a great big warm cuddle

Geminis never
stop talking even
when they're
Doing It

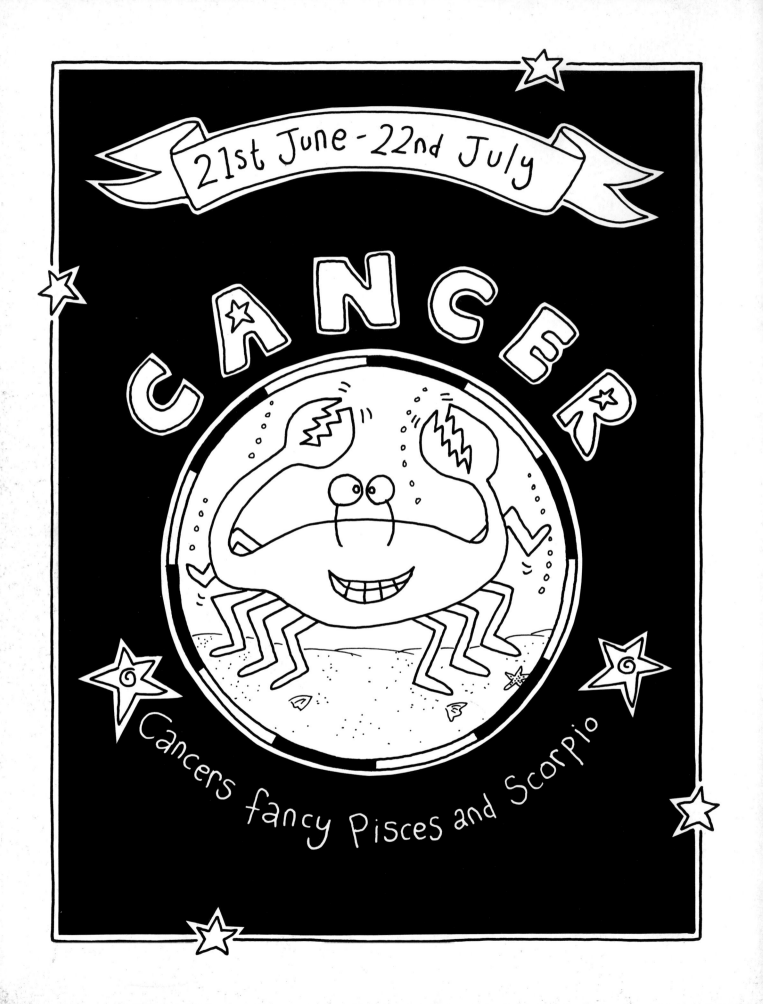

Cancer

They're sensitive, gentle and caring
They want you to have a good time
If you fart in their bed
Or throw up on their head
They say "It's alright I don't mind"

Cancer Looks

Some Cancers have great big bellies cos they like stuffing their faces infront of the T.V. Others are skinny and weedy with knobbly knees and legs like chickens

Cancer Men like to wear raggy old clothes. They have baby faces and goofy teeth cos they suck their thumbs a lot

Cancer Women look sexy and mysterious. They either have no bosoms at all or giant great wobbly ones

Cancer Character

What Cancers like most is being in a happy home. They get very soppy about the past and they love spending lots of time with their families

Cancers do too much worrying and they often turn tiny problems into gigantic disasters

Cancer and Friends

Cancer people love nothing better than nattering about the old times with a few good friends

Secretly Cancers are worried that everyone thinks they're rubbish

Cancer people make brilliant LOVE DOCTORS because:-

1. They are very caring and love looking after people

my friend wants to snog you

2. They like to feel needed

oh Love Doctor Love Doctor you're my only hope

moi?

girlie in distress →

DOCTOR ♥

3. They are more interested in other people than in themselves

So tell me your problems

Well, it all started when Maisy scribbled on my pants

Cancer and Love

Warning:- unless you give a Cancer masses of love and cuddles they will go all silly and babyish

Cancers often fall in love with people who have got piles of money

Once a Cancer knows you love them they will be incredibly soppy with you all the time

Cancer and Sex

Most Cancer people are brilliant in bed and like to learn all about your favourite Love Tricks

Cancers are worried about catching diseases so they always wear lots of protection

⭐ Special Tip ⭐

If you want to Do It with a Cancer you must make sure they don't bring their Mum along with them

Leo

They like to have fun and be happy
They're carefree and noisy and proud
They sing naughty songs at the top
of their voices
And never stop farting out loud

Leo Looks

Leos love it when people look at them so they always try to be as gorgeous and beautiful as they can

Leo Men are often tall and thin with strong muscles. They have loud voices and giant doodahs

Leo Women have beautiful faces, sexy eyes and loads of long wavy hair. They like to dress up in saucy undies

Leo Character

Leos are the happiest and smiliest people in the world. What they like most is partying being silly and having fun

But sometimes, especially when they have drunk loads of booze, Leos can turn into loud bossy show-offs

Leo and Friends

Leos have loads of mates for mucking around with...

... but only one or two bestest friends for sharing their special secrets with

Most Leos would love to be POP STARS because:-

1. They like people to tell them how fantastic they are

2. They are brilliant at spending loads of money

3. They love leaping around and making lots of noise

Leo and Love

Leo is the most romantic star sign of all and people who are Leos fall <u>very</u> <u>deeply</u> in love

A Leo who loves you will give you millions of presents and won't ever think of Doing It with anyone else EVER

Warning :-

If you do not love a Leo as much as a Leo loves you his heart will be broken for ever

Leo and Sex

Leos love:-

STROKING

TICKLING

HUGGING

Take off your trousers and lie down now!

When it comes to Doing It Leos always like to be in charge

☆ **Special Tip** ☆

A Leo who wants you for sex will want you for love and friendship as well

Virgo

Virgos are fussy and boring
They like to be tidy and neat
But the second they jump
At some rumpety-pump
They do it like hippos on heat

❀ Virgo Looks ❀

Virgos are shy and quiet so you must not look at them for too long or they will go red and sweaty and start shuffling their feet

Virgo Men have bulging tummies, specs and ginormous heads for fitting all their brains in

Virgo Women have beautiful eyes, tidy hairstyles and boring clothes

❀ Virgo Character ❀

Virgos are incredibly brainy. They love facts and they often know all sorts of rubbish about everything

Virgos prefer reading books and having grown-up conversations to going to parties

❀ Virgo and Friends ❀

Virgos can take their time to make friends because they sometimes seem snotty and rude when all they are is shy

Virgos are kind and helpful and good at looking after their friends

Virgos would make good GROWN-UP BUSINESS PEOPLE because :-

1. They love working and are very interested in sums and computers

blip bang

try the super zonka whoopee program

EXECUTIVE

SUMS CHARTS GIRLS FOOTIE

2. They like making lists and putting things in order

TODAY
7.30 - Get up
7.45 - Go to Lav
8.00 - Brush teeth
8.15 - Breakfast
Bus
lift
eeting
11.15 -

9.30 - Go to Lav again
9.45 - cup of tea
10.00 - write letters
10.15 - smile at Norman
10.30 - Brush hair
10.45 - Eat Biscuits
11.00 - Go to Lav

3. They are very sensible with money and love saving it up in little piles

hee hee

SAVINGS

SWEETS BOOZE

DISCOS

❀ Virgo and Love ❀

Virgos think falling in love is silly and that there are more important things to be getting on with

Virgos choose their lovers with their heads and not their hearts

Warning:-

If your lover is a Virgo you will have to put up with lots of nagging and fussiness

✿ Virgo and Sex ✿

Virgos can go for ages without having sex but once they find someone they fancy, they want to Do It with them till their bits drop off

Virgos like to do things properly so don't be surprised if they get out a book of instructions

⭐ Special Tip ⭐

Most of all Virgos like Doing It in the shower because it's clean and tidy and doesn't mess up the bed

☆ Libra Looks ☆

As soon as you look at a Libran you think they're lovely which is why Librans spend so much time looking at themselves

short and curlies

saucy bottom

Libra Men have voices that make girls go all swoony. They like to comb the hair on their dangly bits and they <u>always</u> wear clean pants

Libra Women have curvy bodies, sexy faces and the scrumptiousest smiles in the world

☆ Libra Character ☆

Librans want everything to be beautiful and lovely. They adore grown-up music, gorgeous outfits, pretty pictures and twirly dancing

Librans are totally useless at making up their minds

☆ Libra and Friends ☆

Librans hate being on their own so they always go everywhere with lots of friends

Warning:-

Librans love nattering and they are never stuck for things to say

Librans would make good FASHION DESIGNERS because:-

1. They love arty type stuff and like to make everything match

2. They are often moody and stroppy and easy to upset

Boo hoo hoo my beautiful outfit is ruined

3. They prefer to be neat and clean and tidy to sweaty and dirty and messy

Poo-ee

whiff

FAB GEAR

☆ Libra and Love ☆

Librans love the idea of being in love and they long to be swept off their feet

Love for a Libran is more about friendly cuddles than mad snogging and passionate sex

Librans like to look good so they usually fall in love...

...with very beautiful people...

...or very ugly people

✯ Libra and Sex ✯

Librans love flirting and are brilliant at making you want to Do It with them

✯ Special Tip ✯

Some Librans prefer reading about sex to actually Doing It

But when a Libran wants to Do It with you they like to make sure it's the best sex you've ever had

Scorpio

If you want to kiss and hug
They get in such a muddle
They'd always rather do rude things
Than have a soppy cuddle

Scorpio Looks

Scorpios have hypnotic eyes that stare straight into your brain and see all your privatest thoughts and rudest secrets

Scorpio Men are either very handsome or very ugly. They have hairy backs and they fiddle with their privates all the time

Scorpio Women have a special look that makes you want to tear off your clothes and leap into bed with them straight away

Scorpio Character

Scorpios will do anything to be the best. They hate weedy people and they always get what they want

They are also sneaky and mysterious and they love thinking up cunning plans

☼Scorpio and Friends

Scorpios are difficult to make friends with because...

1 They are suspicious of strangers

good morning

I bet he wants my chips

2 They hate being told when they are wrong

you should have turned left

SHUT UP!

MAP

☆ Special Tip ☆

You can always trust a Scorpio to keep safe all your naughtiest secrets

pssst...I'm not wearing any pants

whisper

Scorpios would be brilliant SECRET AGENTS because:-

1. They are tough and brave and daring and love going on missions

2. They like being horrid to people who get in their way

3. They like to travel to far away places and see new things

Scorpio and Love

Scorpios find it difficult to talk about what they're feeling inside

warning:-

Scorpios love revenge so if you ever Do It with anyone else they will chase after you and chop off your bits

Scorpios find falling in love difficult but once they start they will love you for ever and ever

Scorpio and Sex

Scorpios are crazy about rude sex because it lets out all their bottled up feelings

Warning:- Scorpios can suddenly feel like Doing It at the strangest moments

Scorpios love flirting and talking about all sorts of rude things

Sagittarius!

Although they are kind and amusing
They do have some horrible habits
Like scratching their bottoms
And eating their bogies
And saying rude words to small rabbits

Sagittarius Looks

Sagittarians have a cheeky look as if they are just about to do something very wicked which they probably are

Sagittarian Men have good bodies that look like they do masses of exercise. They have happy faces and they often wear posing pants

Sagittarian Women have bright twinkly eyes and freaky hairstyles. Most of them like to wear funky clothes

Sagittarius Character

What Sagittarians like most of all is freedom. They need to travel and discover new people and places all over the World

Sagittarians hate to live normal boring lives and love to get into all sorts of weird and groovy stuff

☙ Sagittarius and Friends ↗

Sagittarians are great fun to be with. They are clever and witty and can never resist telling a good joke

Warning:-

Sagittarians are useless at keeping secrets and they often say things without really thinking

Sagittarians make good EXLORERS and ADVENTURERS because:-

1. They are brave and daring and love challenges and risks

splash
speed
touch me and you'll be handbags matey!
grrr
grrr

more tea
tug
yum

2. They hate grown-up offices and like doing things their own way

3. They are always smiley and love to see the best in everything

chomp munch
it's okay, I'm left-handed

Sagittarius and Love

Sagittarians are warm and loving and friendly and cuddly

But they need their space and don't like the idea of settling down

Warning :-

If you are in love with a Sagittarian make sure you go on loads of soppy holidays or they won't love you for very long

Sagittarius and Sex

When it comes to Doing It Sagittarians love to experiment and try out all sorts of new things

Some Sagittarians like to have lots of lovers at the same time

☆ Special Tip ☆

Sagittarians always feel sexy in aeroplanes

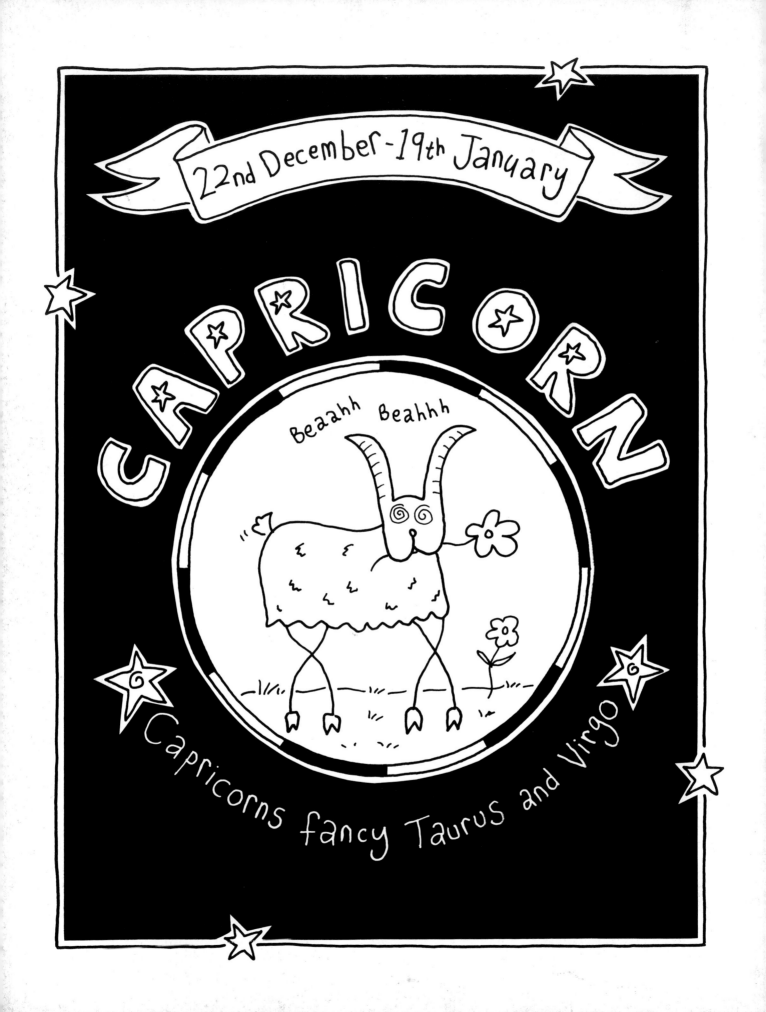

Capricorn

They want everything to be perfect

So think they're too fat or too tall

They always take off all their clothes in the dark

Cos they're worried their bits are too small

Capricorn Looks

Capricorns look serious and proper. They like old-fashioned style clothes and some of them have ginormous noses

Capricorn Men often look older than they are. They have smart hairstyles and are not very good at smiling

Capricorn Women have sexy legs and big bosoms which they like to cover up because they think bosoms are rude

Capricorn Character

Capricorns are very grown-up and sensible. A Capricorn at a party will drink a small shandy and go to bed at 10 o'clock

Capricorns have lots of hobbies and interests which other people don't always find so interesting

𝔈 Capricorn and Friends 𝔈

Capricorn friends are kind and gentle and they always like to help

Capricorns never do bottom burps because they hate people laughing at them and they are much too polite anyway

Capricorns would make good TEACHERS and BANK MANAGERS because:-

1. They are only happy when they can make rules and be in charge

titter

squelch

rule 24(c) - no bogey flicking in class

it's mine all mine hee hee hee

"stuff"

2. They are very stingy and love saving up all their money

3. They hate lazing around and love organising all sorts of things

sulk

Miss!

boring!

O.k everyone spread out... I'm bowler

Capricorn and Love

Capricorns can talk about all sorts of brainy things but when it comes to love they go all mumbly and waffly

Warning:-

Some Capricorns get love and work muddled up and think they're the same thing

But underneath, Capricorns long for the perfect relationship full of soppy fluffy moments and a warm happy ending

Capricorn and Sex

Secretly Capricorns would love to tear off their clothes and go crazy dancing under the stars and snogging all night long

But they never would in real life because:-

They think kissing with your mouths open gives you germs

They would be worried about getting sand up their bottoms

Aquarius

They're bad at expressing their feelings
And bottle them all up inside
But when they're in love
They say "Heavens above
I'm all wonky and googly-eyed"

☆ Aquarius Looks ☆

If you see someone who looks like they have just landed from another planet you are probably looking at an Aquarius

Aquarius Men have a big friendly happy smile. They often go bald quickly and they love dressing up in girl's undies

Aquarius Women look incredibly gorgeous and totally weird at the same time. They don't like normal clothes so they often dress in loony styles

☆ Aquarius Character ☆

Aquarius people are totally unique. They think in crazy ways that no-one else understands and they are often miles ahead of their time

Aquarians love having loads of ideas about changing the world

♒ Aquarius and Friends ♒

Aquarian people are fun to muck around with and they always have a groovy mixture of friends

But they are not very good if you want to sit down on your own with them and sort out all your problems

pickled brain

Aquarians would make good NUTTY INVENTORS because:-

1. They love science and gadgets and anything to do with the future

2. They hate normal jobs and are often best at working on their own

3. They look at everything they come across in a new way

Aquarius and Love

Aquarians who look for love will want someone who will understand the way they think

Warning:-
Aquarius people hate talking about their own feelings but they love finding out about yours

The more space you give an Aquarius to do their own thing the more they will love you

This can be quite difficult

Aquarius and Sex

Aquarians are brilliant at snogging but when it comes to Doing It they get all shy and embarrassed

⭐ Special Tip. ⭐

If you want to Do It with an Aquarian you must tell them it's their brains you fancy them for

Sex with an Aquarian is never normal

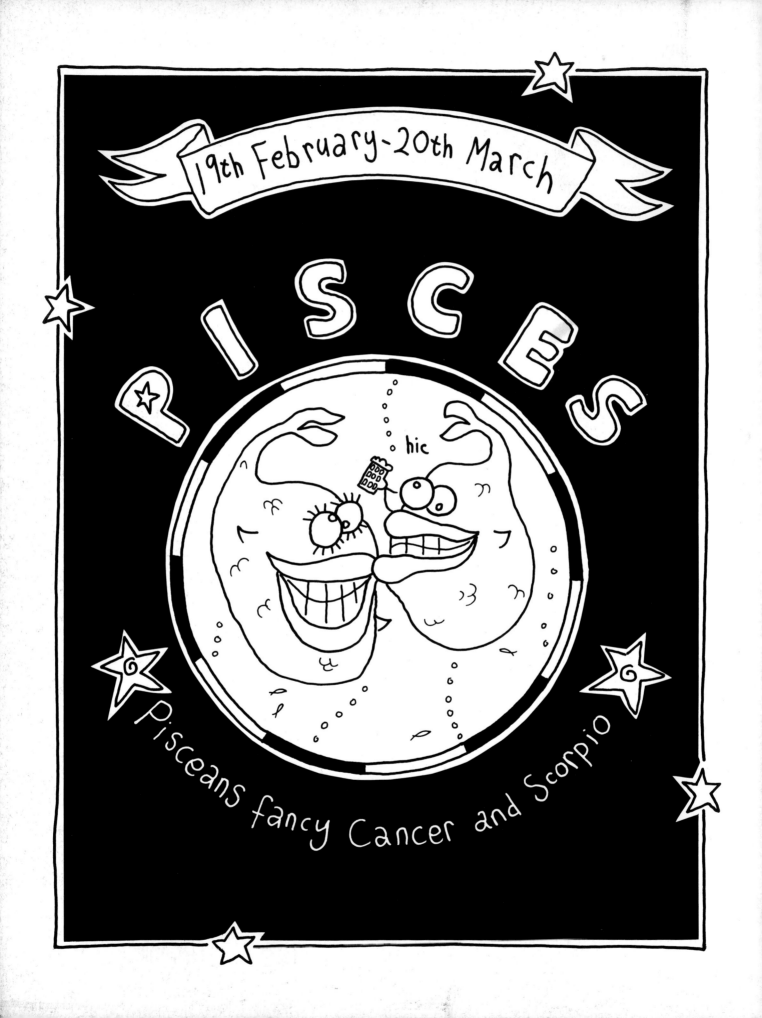

Pisces

They like to get drunk and go naked
They're always ahead of the trends
They cover their bellies
With ice-cream and jellies
And try to snog all of their friends

ꙮ Pisces Looks ꙮ

Pisces people have a spacey far-away look as if they have just snogged the sexiest person in the world

whiff

oops!

v. drafty

Pisces Men like to wear weird arty-type clothes. They have lovely friendly eyes and sometimes they have mould growing in-between their toes

Pisces Women smile at you in a way that makes you go all soft and gooey inside. They often forget to wear any pants

ꙮ Pisces Character ꙮ

No-one knows what goes on inside a Pisces person's head. They are dreamy and mysterious and they like to wander off into their own little world

skippy dippy doodah twiddly diddly dum dum

A Pisces person can be :-

A barmy-headed scatterbrain

blabber blabber

or a total and utter genius

remarkable!

Wooo

usually they are a mixture of both

Pisces and Friends

ooh you're such a lovely lovely lovely man!

Pisces people can make total strangers feel like their bestest friend in the whole wide world

They have a funny way of knowing what you're thinking

letsssss go aaand...

hic

... get a giant double vindaloo special with extra hot curry sauce

weird!

which is just as well because they like to get so pissed with you that no-one can say anything anyway

Pisces people make good ARTISTS WRITERS and MUSICIANS because :-

1. They have smashing imaginations and like to escape to a world of make-believe

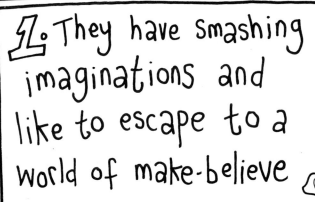

2. They love music and have to listen to it all the time

3. They can suddenly change from feeling very happy to very sad

Pisces and Love

Pisces people are incredibly romantic and they often show this in ways you don't expect

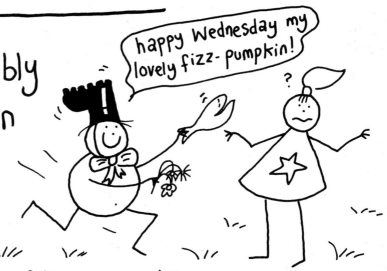

A Piscean wants the whole world to be happy so they give lots of love but they need lots of love too

<u>Warning</u>: It can be difficult having a Pisces lover because you never know what they're going to do next

Pisces and Sex

Pisceans are not sex-mad and they only like Doing It with people who they love

saucy ladies of the night

tempt

tempt

Pisces people have loads of secret rude fantasies

flash

strip

snog

☆ Special Tip ☆

A Pisces always loves Doing It underwater

wiggle

wiggle